P9-CEL-980

GOOD DOG, CARL

By
Alexandra Day

GREEN TIGER PRESS
La Jolla • London

To H.D., who has never let us forget about Ponies

A
Star & Elephant
Book

First Edition • Fifth Printing
Library of Congress Catalog Card Number: 85-070419
ISBN: 0-88138-062-8 (Hardbound)

"Look after the baby, Carl.
I'll be back shortly."

LAUNDRY

CRÈME
ÉCLIPSE
CIRAGE A LA CIRE
DUCKS IN THE POND

WHEAT BREAD
BUTTER

HERSHEY'S
SYRUP

Cereal
cream

cream
BUTTER

"Good dog, Carl!"

A salute to the creator of Münchener Bilderbogen *No. 1001, and thanks to Molly Myers and Toby for their sitting talent.*

The paintings for this book were executed in egg tempera.
Color separations by Photolitho, AG, Gossau/Zurich, Switzerland.
Printed and bound in Hong Kong.

G.A.R. MEMORIAL LIBRARY, WEST NEWBURY
3 2135 00004 690 0